To Ava, Mackenlee, and Hudson

Searching feverishly was Olivia the Owl.
Looking everywhere, she was on the prowl.
She had forgotten where she'd hidden her loot!
She remembered it was buried under a nearby tree root.
She nervously pecked with her tired, sore beak
At elm tree, oak tree, and even a teak.
Finally! She recovered her draw-string purse!
"My beak's all bent, but it could have been worse!"

Owls hunt at night. They have excellent hearing and keen vision. Owls can turn their heads ¾ of the way around. They swoop down with silent wings to catch their prey.[1]

Portia the Parakeet perched on a rafter.

She was surely the ultimate, skillful crafter.

She showed much talent with sequins and glue.

There wasn't a project that she couldn't do!

She could wallpaper, quilt, or tile a floor.

She could totally transform your home décor!

Portia the Parakeet's business card reads:

"Call Portia for all of your domestic needs."

Parakeets live in rainforests and dense savanna. They eat seeds, fruits, nuts, berries and buds from a variety of plants. Pairs nest in high hollows of tree trunks.[2]

If you open your window you might certainly hear
catie the canary serenading so clear.
She's the finest with tempo, diction, and pitch.
There's nothing at all you'd want to switch.
She'll sing for bar mitzvahs and parties galore.
At weddings and reunions, the notes will just pour.
So when the need arises and you must host,
call catie the canary—famous from coast to coast!

Canaries have been bred for color, song type and form. The female lays 4-5 eggs and incubates for two weeks. During that time, she never leaves the nest,and depends on her mate to bring her food.[3]

Fillipe the Flamingo likes to strut his stuff—
All pink and orange feathers and fluff.
Every morning, stretching, from his nest he arises.
He grooms his plumes, which he highly prizes.
At water's edge, with beak toward sky,
Fillipe boasts, "There's no finer flamingo than I!"
With one bent knee, he assumes his pose.
"I'm the brightest and best. I think everyone knows."

American Flamingos have brilliant feathers that range from pale pink to a deep scarlet red. They get their coloring from the microscopic shrimp and algae in their diet.[4]

Anton the Arctic Tern was a Soviet.

The USA was his new safety net.

"This is great!" he exclaimed. "Old Glory and apple pie!"

"But someone might think I'm an international spy!"

So he learned to speak English, southern-style.

Now no one would think he was a vile exile.

He learned to play baseball instead of chess.

Then he memorized the Gettysburg Address.

The Arctic Tern is a small, slender gray-and-white bird. It is well known for its long yearly migration. It travels from its Arctic breeding grounds to Antarctica where it enjoys the Antarctic summer, covering around 25,000 miles roundtrip.[5]

Gavin the Goose liked baby food.
When given steak, he became "unglued."
His anxious mother would get so undone,
But he wouldn't even peck at a hamburger bun.
He was six years old but refused to chew.
He acted like he was just one or two!
The only way to make him hush,
Was to give him apple, prune, or oatmeal mush!

The big, black-necked Canada Goose, with its signature white chinstrap mark is a familiar and widespread bird of fields and parks. Some migratory populations are not going as far south in the winter as they used to. This shift has been due to changes in farm practices and milder weather.[6]

Calvin the Crow lived in Oklahoma.

He moved there to get a college diploma.

When he bought his books, he dove in headfirst,

Studying 'round the clock, he was fully immersed.

He would memorize, write essays, and always review.

Other pastimes, he did not pursue.

Finally, he graduated with a 4.0.

Then, he gave the college dorm the old heave-ho.

The American Crow builds a large stick nest well-hidden in the crotch of a tree or on a horizontal limb, usually an evergreen. They eat fruits, nuts, seeds, and insects and other invertebrates. They also enjoy food scraps from humans.[7]

Penny the Pigeon lived in the inner city.

Things were run down. It was kind of gritty.

No green lawns; it was pretty weedy.

Her building's walls were filled with graffiti.

She cried out, "It's not fit for the human race!"

"This building surely has become a disgrace!"

So she painted and nailed and planted some flowers.

Now it looks better than Manhattan's Trump Towers!

Pigeons nest on buildings and window ledges. In the countryside they also nest on barns and grain towers, under bridges, and on natural cliffs. Pigeons can find their way home, even if released from a distant location blindfolded. They navigate by sensing the earth's magnetic fields, as well as by sound and smell.[8]

Thelma the Thrush belonged to Girl Scouts.
But instead of selling cookies,
        she tried to hawk brussels sprouts.
"Come on, people! Give them a chance!"
But the crowds looked away without a glance.
"They come in green with a yummy nice crunch!"
"They taste delicious with strawberry punch!"
"They're a super food," she would proudly defend.
But she couldn't sell any, not even to her best friend.

The Wood Thrush is a songster, and it can sing "internal duets" with itself. The male Wood Thrush does more feeding of the chicks than the female, freeing her up to start a second brood.[9]

Peppi the Pelican wore gigantic, huge shoes.
He tripped a lot and usually had a purple bruise.
He heard one day about a really big race—
He wanted to enter but thought he'd be a disgrace.
But, alas, he signed up and decided to try.
He yelled, "No pics!" (He was camera-shy.)
He started to run, and then hit his stride.
At the end of the race...wow! He'd won by a landslide!

Pelicans are large, bulky waterbirds with webbed feet, short legs, and a remarkably long bills. When hunting, they spot their prey from the air and plunge into the water head-first. After trapping the fish, they drain the water out the sides of the bill and then swallow the fish whole.[10]

Otto the Oriole pecked at a stale hotdog bun.

Blech! Gag! "This is not fit for anyone!"

"It's not fit for man nor beast!"

"If I don't watch out, I'll soon be deceased!"

"Wait, what aroma wafts across the avenue?"

"Ooh, (sniff, sniff) it's yummy barbecue!"

"I'm heading that way without hesitation."

"I'm not waiting for an invitation!"

Baltimore Orioles sometimes use their slender beaks to feed in an unusual way, called "gaping": they stab the closed bill into soft fruits, then open their mouths to cut a juicy swath from which they drink with their brushy-tipped tongues.[11]

Galileo the Gull had been aboard Noah's ark!
"That," he'll tell you, "was no theme park!"
Some days he would let down his fishing pole,
(Except when lightning flashed and
                          the thunder would roll).

After 40 days, he saw some much-welcomed sunshine!
And, hey, what's that? A little skyline!
When they disembarked, they'd have a new address.
Where would that be? It was anyone's guess!

*Gulls are often thought of as coastal birds, but some
are also common in inland areas. Young California
Gulls practice their hunting skills by dropping a stick
in midair and swooping down to catch it.*[12]

Carl the Cockatoo owns a barbershop.

Snip, snip, chop goes the curly top!

He cuts anyone's hair, be it brunettes or blondes.

He trims bankers and plumbers and even ex-cons!

"He has skillful hands," say his clientele,

"It's like being under a magic spell!"

So when you need a cut, be it braids or a crew,

Come see Carl for an excellent new "do"!

The Cockatoo uses its powerful bill to eat very hard seeds and nuts that other species can't access, like palm nuts. They are also among the loudest of all parrots, and communicate by whistling contact calls.[13]

Rosette the Robin spent a year overseas.
She learned to speak French as quick as a breeze.
She soon became a Paris fashion plate,
But then...she began to put on weight.
Flaky French pastries had become her downfall.
She began to have problems with her cholesterol.
Where can you find her every lunch hour?
Munching an éclair beside the Eiffel tower.

Robins build their nests with grasses, twigs and mud. They've been known to eat more than 60 worms a day. They also eat insects and berries.[14]

Burt the Buzzard was an international sleuth.

He'd uncover villains and they'd confess to the truth.

When a call came for help, he'd pack his suitcase,

Always hoping it wouldn't be a wild goose chase.

He might head for France, Spain, or even Beirut.

Culprits ran, with Burt in hot pursuit.

He'd nab them and send them home airmail,

Straight away to the city jail!

The Buzzard is a common large hawk, often seen soaring. They favor woodland and forest edge, and farmland with hedges; they are also found in towns with larger trees and wooded parks.[15]

Stan the Sandpiper likes to tan on the beach.
To say his skin is like leather is not a far reach.
All summer long he pours on suntan lotion,
But it's only SPF 10, not a magic potion!
His beak and feathers are mostly fried.
If they're not, he's just not satisfied.
He thinks he looks like a handsome beach bum,
But really it's more like a big dried plum.

The Spotted Sandpiper is the most widespread sand-piper in North America. The male takes the primary role in parental care, incubating the eggs and taking care of the young.[16]

Pamela the Peacock summoned her personal chauffeur.
"I'm in desperate need of a manicure!"
She sat in the limousine with a fingernail file.
I think that car was as long as a mile!
As her nails were being painted, she chirped,
                    "Please add glitter!"
"Hmmm," she thought, "maybe I should reconsider."
(I think I should add in her defense:
"Glittery Gold" polish was a little intense.)

Here you see a "peacock," which is the name for the colorfully plumaged male peafowl only. The females are called "peahens" and are actually smaller and more dull in color. The peacock is one of the largest flying birds in the world.[17]

Chandra the Chickadee loved to dance.

She would pirouette, plié, twirl, and prance.

Her skills were certainly above ordinary.

Her real goal was to be a "sugarplum fairy."

On the day of her audition,

She danced for the judges with no inhibition.

When she finished on stage, it was quiet as a church.

Then..."Bravo! You're it! We've ended our search!"

There are several varieties of chickadee. One is called the South Carolina Chickadee, named by John James Audubon. In winter, the Carolina Chickadees live in flocks of two to eight birds and defend areas against other flocks.[18]

Boynton the Barn Swallow was on a cruise
When suddenly, there was some alarmingly bad news!
As he was on the deck playing shuffleboard,
(and handily being hugely outscored),
The huge boat tipped over and began to sink!
This thing was a little rinky-dink!
Now in the ocean, he was thankfully afloat,
Bobbing around on an inflatable lifeboat

Barn Swallows have long, forked tails and slender bodies. They build their nests in barns, under bridges and the eaves of roofs. They hunt for flying insects, like bees, butterflies, and wasps.[19]

41

Niles the Nuthatch created culinary delights.
(Although his chef's coat is now skintight!)
His personal recipe for leg of lamb
Is a winner! Certainly a real grand slam!
Or he can make you a tasty snack—
A yummy chocolate chip flapjack.
When he's in the kitchen, you should not disturb.
Nile's cooking skills are simply superb!

The Red-breasted Nuthatch collects resin globules from cone trees and puts it around the entrance of its nest hole. The male puts the resin primarily around the outside of the hole while the female puts it around the inside. The resin may help to keep out predators. The nuthatch avoids the resin by diving directly through the hole.[20]

Tommy the Scarlet Tanager moved to Brazil.

To get a job, he needed a skill.

He ended up working for a coffee plantation.

Picking coffee beans was his new occupation.

On his days off, he danced the samba.

And when he went swimming, he looked out for piranha!

He eventually became an international exporter.

All in all, he enjoyed life "below the border."

The male Scarlet Tanager is bright red; however the female is olive green. They live in forests and the male and female sing together while making a nest.[21]

Freddie the Finch wanted to be an astronaut.
If he went up in a rocket, he'd be a big shot.
What was it like to walk on the moon?
Was it really just a big sand dune?
Freddie would be famous like Buzz and Neil.
"A step for mankind" would be a really big deal!
And then to look down on Earth below—
That would be a sight he'd never outgrow!

The House Finch was originally a bird of the western United States and Mexico. In 1940 a small number of finches were turned loose on Long Island, New York. They quickly started breeding and spread across almost all of the eastern United States and southern Canada within the next 50 years.[22]

Larry the Lark liked things to be alphabetized.

Anything in sight had to be reorganized.

If he went to the store for milk, corn, and beef,

His list had to read, "beef, corn, and milk," for any relief.

His sock drawer was arranged blue, red, then yellow.

Any other way, and you'd hear him bellow!

When he packed his luggage to go on trips,

He arranged like this: comb, then pants, then q-tips!

Larks have a melodious call, and it is mentioned often in literature and music. Their bills work well for cracking seeds open and digging in order to obtain food.[23]

Barclay the Blackbird was a farmer whose plants
wouldn't grow.

His corn came up to his pinky toe.

So he asked, "what gives?" to the crop advisor.

That man said, "You need to add fertilizer!"

Soon his veggies were a work of art!

(They grew so huge, despite their false start.)

If you have a taste for something good to eat,

Go to Barclay's farm for a tasty treat!

Blackbirds are sometimes eliminated around agricultural fields in an attempt to protect crops. Although they do eat grains, their appetite for insects makes them more of a farmer's friend than a pest. Blackbirds are social birds that nest in colonies of up to 100 birds.[24]

Endnotes and Acknowledgments

1. [Owl] Kurki, Kim, *World of Birds* (Black Dog & Leventhal Publishers, Inc., 2014), p. 31.

2. [Parakeet] https://www.aviary.org/birds-habitats/our-birds/?search=parakeet

3. [Canary] https://www.aviary.org/birds-habitats/our-birds/?search=canary

4. [Flamingo] https://www.aviary.org/birds-habitats/our-birds/?search=flamingo

5. [Arctic Tern] https://www.allaboutbirds.org/guide/Arctic_Tern

6. [Goose] https://www.allaboutbirds.org/guide/Canada_Goose/

7. [Crow] https://www.aviary.org/birds-habitats/our-birds/?search=crow

8. [Pigeon] https://www.allaboutbirds.org/guide/Rock_Pigeon/

9. [Thrush] https://www.allaboutbirds.org/guide/Wood_Thrush/

10. [Pelican] https://www.aviary.org/birds-habitats/our-birds/?search=pelican

11. [Oriole] https://www.allaboutbirds.org/guide/Baltimore_Oriole/

12. [Gull] https://www.allaboutbirds.org/guide/California_Gull/

13. [Cockatoo] https://www.aviary.org/birds-habitats/our-birds/?search=cockatoo

14. [Robin] Kurki, Kim, *World of Birds* (Black Dog & Leventhal Publishers, Inc., 2014), pp. 14, 15. Photograph: en:User:Mdf, CC BY-SA 3.0 <http://creativecommons.org/licenses/by-sa/3.0/>, via Wikimedia Commons

15. [Buzzard] https://ebird.org/species/combuz1

16. [Sandpiper] https://www.allaboutbirds.org/guide/Spotted_Sandpiper/

17. [Chickadee] https://www.allaboutbirds.org/guide/Carolina_Chickadee/

18. [Peacock] https://www.sciencekids.co.nz/sciencefacts/animals/peacock.html

19. [Barn Swallow] Beer, Julie, *Birds* (National Geographic Society, 2016), p. 103.

20. [Nuthatch] https://www.allaboutbirds.org/guide/Red-breasted_Nuthatch/

21. [Scarlet Tanager] Beer, Julie, *Birds* (National Geographic Society, 2016) p. 138.

22. [Finch] https://www.allaboutbirds.org/guide/House_Finch/

23. [Lark] https://carolinabirds.org/HTML/Lark.htm

24. [Blackbird] https://www.allaboutbirds.org/guide/Brewers_Blackbird/est. Photograph: By Alan D. Wilson - naturespicsonline.com ([1]), CC BY-SA 3.0, https://commons.wikimedia.org/w/index.php?curid=3179252

CPSIA information can be obtained
at www.ICGtesting.com
Printed in the USA
BVHW021723111021
618685BV00002B/64